G000300565

nearly 10 years on no1
the Yobs strip is stil
strong. Unfortunately so
are Yobs in the flesh and
blood and teeth. Still you
cant have everything. Hope
you enjoy the book.

   Best wishes Tony

Dedicated to the
memory and work of
PETER COOK

SON of YOBS

BY
Tony Husband

PRIVATE EYE • CORGI

These jokes originally appeared in Private Eye.
Published in Great Britain by Private Eye Productions Ltd., 6 Carlisle Street, London W1V 5RG
in association with Corgi Books.

©1995 Pressdram Ltd. ISBN 0 552 14404 5
Designed by Bridget Tisdall. Printed in England by Ebenezer Baylis & Son Ltd, Worcester.

Corgi Books are published by Transworld Publishers Ltd 61–63 Uxbridge Road, Ealing, London W5 5SA
in Australia by Transworld Publishers (Australia) Pty, Ltd 15–23 Helles Avenue, Moorebank, NSW 2170
and in New Zealand by Transworld Publishers (N.Z.) Ltd 3 William Pickering Drive, Albany, Auckland.
2 4 6 8 10 9 7 5 3 1

"I think we've found the big central defender we've been looking for"

"Apparently they're friends of your father from the golf club"

"Oh, Mr Gilbert... I'm afraid Mr Morton's out at the moment. He sends his regrets, however, and asks me to inform you that you're fired"

"He says he's just browsing"

"Don't you think a chandelier's too much for this room?"

"Why do you call your neighbours the 'Wibbly-Wobblies'?"

"...'scuse me. Just how far out of the way is this out-of-the-way place?"

"Ah well! Another day, another set of underpants!"

"The sun has got his hat on, hip hip hip hooray..."

"Damp's a bit of a problem in these houses"

"Forget the critics, Max! You're a damn fine illusionist"

"Hello, we've just moved in next door. Can you lend us £5,000?"

"He's been under a bit of stress"

"So, you're the boy who wants to be a bellringer"

"Nigel's one of the top salesmen at the cigarette company"

"Ah you've found the corner with the little quicksand problem"

"Harold? Oh, he's in the garden"

"...and for your own sake, too, Philip, you'll have to accept he's not a baby any more..."

"I think you'll like the home brew…"

"Go away and never darken my door again!"

"Before you take my daughter's hand in marriage I've set up a little test for you..."

"Believe me, children, if Mummy and Daddy could sort this out
any other way we would"

"Mum, Dad... I'm a homo sapien"

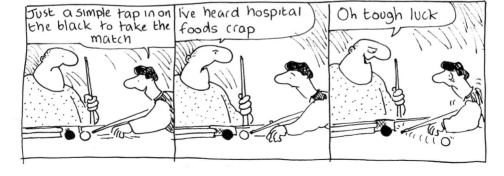

"I'm not being funny, Gerald, but couldn't we just play Scrabble?"

"Good day. Could I interest you in our PEPs scheme?"

"Curse those Mountain Penny-Farthings!"

"Oh, George was reared by hamsters"

"You can't fool me, Daniel. The budgie's dead, isn't it?"

"I'm afraid we can't afford wages any more, so could you queue up with a bowl…"

"Mrs Pringle, bring me a 20-pence piece from petty cash, would you…"

"I see he's got his father's legs"

"We've got a very thorough Crime Watch organisation in this street"

"Bill, he'll go to sleep when he's ready"

"Damn it! He's found my dentures again"